Little RASCAL

by STERLING NORTH

Illustrated by CARL BURGER

SCHOLASTIC BOOK SERVICES
NEW YORK • TORONTO • LONDON • AUCKLAND • SYDNEY • TOKYO

Text copyright, ©, 1965 by Sterling North. Illustrations copyright, ©, 1965 by
Carl Burger. This edition is published by Scholastic Book Services, a division of
Scholastic Magazines, Inc., by arrangement with E. P. Dutton & Co., Inc.,
New York, N. Y.

16 15 14 13 12 11 10   9/7 0 1 2 3/8
                    Printed in U.S.A.   11

For Randy, Christina, Gregory, and Jeffrey
with the love and admiration
of a fond grandfather

Summer

SUMMER

How do you feed a baby raccoon weighing less than one pound?

Some children feed them with a medicine dropper or a doll's nursing bottle. But I fed my tiny raccoon through a clean straw. I took warm milk in my mouth, then tilted the hollow straw downward to his mouth and watched him suck eagerly.

I called my raccoon "Rascal," because he was such a mischief. He had gleaming black eyes, a mask like a little bandit, and five black rings around his fluffy tail. His whispered trills were full of wonder and curiosity. In the wide-spreading oak tree behind our house there was a comfortable hole which made a good home for Rascal. Here he dreamed away his first two months, sleeping happily between feedings.

At the foot of this great tree lay my big Saint Bernard, Wowser. He was a dependable watchdog who protected all my pets:

My little woodchucks!

My good little black and white skunks in their cages!

My cats of many colors!

And even my wicked pet crow named Poe, who liked to steal every shining object he could find and hide these treasures in the belfry of the Methodist Church.

Wowser was a handsome animal weighing one hundred and seventy pounds. It would have been a brave dog or a foolish boy who tried to disturb Wowser's new friend, my little raccoon Rascal.

One day in June, when cherries were ripe and the whole world cheerful with bird song, Wowser and I heard a quavering trill at the hole in the tree. A moment later we saw two bright eyes shining from a small black mask. Rascal was peering from the door of his home at the world below, and soon he began backing down the tree like a little bear, tail first.

Wowser was worried. He yelped a question or two and glanced up to see what I thought about this new problem. I told my dog not to worry, but to watch what happened.

I had a shallow minnow pool not far from the tree. Rascal hurried to the little pond and started fishing. His sensitive hands searched the shallows, while his eyes gazed far away as though he were thinking of something else entirely. Soon his clever little hands caught a minnow. He began washing it back and forth, as raccoons do with almost everything they eat. Rascal carried his minnow to the edge of the pool, very pleased with himself, and began eating the small fish in polite little nibbles. Then he started exploring the back yard surrounding the oak tree. Once he pounced on a cricket. A moment later he lay very still while the dark shadow of Poe-the-Crow swept across the grass. When Rascal came too near to the edge of our green lawn, Wowser pushed him back, firmly but gently.

Having explored his little world, my raccoon climbed the tree and disappeared into his safe home in the hollow of the oak. He seemed to be perfectly satisfied with his first trip abroad. Wowser sighed with relief. Rascal was again safely in his nest. He had not hurt himself, nor run away. Perhaps he would not be the problem that Wowser had feared.

Being a Rascal-sitter was a twenty-four-hour-a-day job.

My father and I lived alone together in a ten-room

house in the little town of Brailsford Junction in southern Wisconsin. My mother was dead, and my two older sisters, Theo and Jessica, were living elsewhere. My big brother, Herschel, was with the American Army in France, fighting against the Germans in World War I.

My father was very kind to me. He let me build my canoe in the living room, keep any number of pets, and wander as free as the wind over meadows and hills. I knew that he would not object to having Rascal eat with us at the table. From the attic I carried down the family high chair, last used when I was a baby.

At breakfast next morning, I put a shallow earthenware bowl of warm milk on the tray of the high chair. Rascal stood in the chair, placing his hands on the edge of the tray. He could reach the milk easily, and he chirred and trilled his satisfaction. He drank his milk, scarcely dribbling a drop. In fact, his table manners were better than those of many children. My father smiled fondly at our new breakfast companion, and I was delighted at Rascal's good behavior.

All went well until I offered the raccoon a lump of sugar. Rascal took it between his two hands and began washing it back and forth in his milk just as

he had washed the minnow. In a moment or two, of course, it melted entirely away, and you could not imagine a more surprised little raccoon.

First he felt all over the bottom of the bowl to see if he had dropped it.

Then he looked in his right hand. No sugar lump!

Next he looked in his left hand. No sugar lump there either!

Finally he turned to me and shrilled a sharp question: Who had stolen his lump of sugar?

When I recovered from my laughter, I gave him a second lump. He evidently thought about washing it, but then a shrewd look came into his shining eyes. He took the sugar directly to his mouth and began munching it happily.

Rascal was a very bright raccoon. When he learned a lesson, he learned it for life. Never again did he try to wash a lump of sugar.

The kitchen screen door had a worn catch and a weak spring. I did not repair them because I wanted my cats to be able to pull the door open to let themselves in, or push it from the inside to let themselves out. Rascal was certain he could do anything that a cat could do. Several times he watched them open the door. Obviously the trick was to hook your claws in the screen and pull. Feeling very proud of himself, he showed the cats that he was as smart as the oldest and wisest tom.

A few nights later I was surprised and delighted to hear Rascal's trill from the pillow beside me. Then I felt his little hands exploring my face. My raccoon baby had climbed down from his hole in the tree and had opened the back screen door. With eyes

that could see in the dark, he had found his way to my downstairs bedroom. There were no very strict rules in our house, as both Rascal and I realized. My raccoon decided the most comfortable place to sleep was with me. He was as clean as any cat, and perfectly housebroken from the start. So for many months we slept together.

I felt less lonesome now when my father went away on business, leaving me all alone in that big ten-room house.

A boy, a bicycle, and a little raccoon. Imagine the adventures we had! Rascal had become a speed demon. He liked nothing better than whizzing down a steep hill. This lovable little creature had the heart of a lion. He liked to stand in the basket of my bicycle with his feet braced wide apart and his hands gripping the front rim of the basket. His natural goggles made him look like a racing driver. His small button of a nose pointed straight into the wind, and his whiskers blew back nearly to his ears, as his ring tail streamed out behind.

Sometimes he shared the bicycle basket with bunches of crimson, white-tipped radishes which I raised in my war garden and sold to the grocery stores.

Once he shared the basket with blooming rose plants I had dug from the garden to transplant on my mother's grave. The white stone merely said:

IN MEMORY OF SARAH ELIZABETH NELSON NORTH
1866 — 1914

Rascal, of course, could not understand why I felt so sad as I planted the roses around that stone.

Sometimes Rascal shared the basket with my box of fishing tackle, when we went to the river to fish.

Often, after these rides, Rascal and I drank strawberry pop. He quickly learned how to lie on his back and hold the bottle in perfect position with all four feet, while he drained the last sweet drop.

I had started to build my canoe in the living room during the previous winter, when it was much too cold to work in the barn. The ribs that ran the length of the canoe were of clear white pine, fragrant and smooth to the touch. The circular ribs were cut from tough water elm from cheeseboxes which the store-keepers had given me. Naturally all this canoe building created some disorder and dust in the living room.

One day when I was at work on the canoe, a big Stutz Bearcat automobile curved up our drive, and out stepped my beautiful married sister Theodora. She had brought along one of her maids and enough luggage so that I knew she intended to stay for a while.

"Theo, Theo!" I shouted happily, running out to embrace her.

"Hello, sonny boy — my, you're all covered with sawdust."

"I'm building a canoe."

"Not in the living room!" Theo was already suspicious.

"Well, you see, Theo, it was too cold in the barn last winter..."

"Merciful heavens!" Theo said. "Now help Jennie with the luggage, and put it in the downstairs bedroom."

I loved this beautiful auburn-haired sister of mine, but I was a little afraid of her, too. She had taught me to jump up like a jack-in-the-box whenever an older person entered the room, and for a time after my mother's death she had dressed me in the Norfolk jackets that were fashionable then. The other boys had laughed at me. At the sight of the living room, she threw up her hands in horror.

"I've never seen such a mess in my life," she said, "but we'll soon fix that. Jennie and I are going to clean this house from top to bottom. And out goes the canoe. We'll hire a full-time housekeeper, if we can find one."

"Can't you just leave us alone?" I asked mournfully. "Anyhow, you're not my mother."

"Oh, sonny boy," she said, fighting back the tears. She came around the end of the canoe and kissed me quite tenderly.

I didn't mind giving Theo my downstairs bedroom, but my little raccoon didn't understand the new arrangement. That evening, after Theo had gone to sleep, Rascal let himself in at the back door and went confidently to our bed and crawled in with Theo.

My father and I, who were sleeping upstairs, heard a blood-curdling yell. We rushed downstairs in our pajamas to find Theo standing on a chair, treed by my little raccoon. Rascal blinked up at this crazy human being who was screeching like a fire siren.

"He always sleeps in this bed," I explained. "He's clean and perfectly harmless."

"You throw that animal right out of the house and hook the screen door so it can't possibly get back in."

"Well, O.K.," I said, "but you're sleeping in Rascal's bed."

"Don't be saucy," Theo said.

I kept the screen door hooked for the next several nights, but one evening I forgot. Just before dawn Rascal opened the screen door and went cautiously to Theo's room. He decided not to crawl in with her. He did, however, prowl quietly around the bedroom and the adjoining bath. On the wide rim of the lavatory he found the most beautiful trinket he had ever stolen: my sister's diamond ring.

Raccoons and crows love shiny things, and Rascal and Poe-the-Crow often fought over treasures I gave to Rascal, such as bright new pennies. Just before dawn I heard a crow-raccoon fight on the back porch. And when Theo said she had lost her ring, I had a theory about what might have happened.

After we had searched the house and yard and gardens, I decided to look in one more place: the belfry of the Methodist Church, where Poe had his nest. I asked kindly Reverend Hooton, the Methodist minister, if I could climb the dark shaft to the belfry, and he said I might. The shaft was filled with cobwebs, and some of the cleats were loose. I was afraid that I might fall, but I could not turn back.

At last I reached the airy little room at the top, with its widely spaced shutters and its view of the town below. I touched the big deep-toned bell which had been tolled forty-seven times for my mother — once for each year of her short life — and which many years later would be tolled ninety-nine times for my father. I remembered the fragrance of hyacinths at my mother's funeral, and for a few minutes I forgot all about Theo's diamond ring.

Then, in a far corner of the belfry, I saw the circle of twigs, leaves, and black feathers that Poe-the-Crow called home. As some people keep their money in their mattress, Poe had made his bed even more uncomfortable with a pile of shining possessions that overran the nest and spilled across

the floor. Here were some of my best glass marbles, my football whistle, scraps of sheet copper, a second key to our Oldsmobile, and, wonder of wonders, Theo's diamond ring.

I put several of the valuable objects in my pocket, but left the worthless junk, knowing that Poe couldn't tell sheet copper from a diamond ring. Poe dropped in at about this time. He cawed and cussed in crow language, acting as though I were the thief and he the honest householder. His angry voice followed me as I went down the shaft and out into the sunlight.

Theo was so happy to have her ring that she did not insist that I take my canoe to the barn. She even postponed the hiring of a full-time house-keeper. She merely fed us delightful meals and, with Jennie's help, left the house shining clean. Then, with a good-bye kiss and a wave of the hand, she was off again, gallant, beautiful, and brave, her auburn hair shining in the sun.

Summer passes all too swiftly for an active boy of eleven. Rascal and I often went fishing below the dam in the river, at Indian Ford. Sometimes I cast for bass and pickerel among the water lilies. More often I fished for big, fighting silver catfish in my favorite hole below a pleasant sand bar in the river. Rascal meanwhile fished in the shallows along the edge of the bar, often seizing a crayfish — those little monsters that look so much like small fresh-water lobsters. These he washed and ate, tail first, with obvious delight.

Despite mowing lawns and working in my war

always found time to read, lying in the
ck and listening to all the sounds of summer:
p-clop of horses' hoofs, the shrilling of the
cicadas, and the murmuring of the birds.

On a few gala occasions, my father would hang
a sign on the office door:

GONE FOR THE DAY

Then, with a picnic basket filled with sandwiches
and a few bottles of cold root beer and pop, my
father and Rascal and I would clamber happily
into the front seat of the big seven-passenger Oldsmobile, with the top back and the windshield down.
All three of us wore goggles — Rascal's being
natural, of course. He liked to perch between us
on the back of the seat, gazing joyfully ahead as my
father shifted from low into second and from
second into high, speeding up the river road toward
Lake Koshkonong.

Here we hunted for Indian arrowheads, explored
the little cave in the limestone at Taylor's Point,
or swam in the cold water. Rascal, although only
three months old, was an excellent swimmer, dog-
paddling along beside us until he grew tired. He
considered me his natural protector when we were

24

in deep water, and would climb on my shoulder or my head for a rest. Often I would float on my back and arch my chest above the water to give him a better resting place. As soon as he had caught his breath, he would dive in again and paddle along bravely through the little waves, as we explored the coves and grassy points along the sandy shore.

Rascal had never been told about turtle eggs, but on our very first trip to the lake his keen nostrils told him that somewhere in this sand was a delightful form of food he had never before tasted. He dug furiously to bring up the eggs, nearly as large as golf balls. They had been laid by a big snapping turtle and left in the warm sand to hatch. Rascal tore the eggs open with his sharp little teeth and gorged until he could not eat another bite.

Then for hours he slept blissfully on the back seat of the car, as we visited several of my father's farms to see how the crops were growing.

Toward the end of July, 1918, we had heard that the fighting was particularly fierce and bloody on the battlefields of France. Our town was suddenly aware of the danger to the American Army as the Germans made their last great drive toward Paris. More gold stars began to appear on the service flags in the windows. I can remember praying that the one star on our service flag would not turn to gold, and that my beloved brother Herschel would somehow come safely home.

There was a great upsurge of patriotism among all the children of Brailsford Junction. The girls were knitting khaki wristlets for the soldiers, and the boys were competing to see who could collect the largest ball of tin foil. I had a little helper in this search. Because tin foil is shiny, Rascal would trundle up one gutter and down another, looking for the gleaming bits of foil.

His only other assistance in the war effort was the help he gave me in my garden. When I hoed, he followed along behind me like a little dog. He also helped me pick peas. But all the peas he picked he kept for himself, opening each pod as though it

were a small clam, and avidly shelling the green
pearls into his mouth.

One serious mistake I made, however, was to
give Rascal his first taste of sweet corn. I twisted a
plump ear from a stalk, stripped back the husk, and
handed the corn to my pet. He went mildly crazy
over sweet corn, and soon learned to pull down a
stalk and help himself to ear after ear. No other
food he had ever tasted compared with this juicy
new delicacy.

When I told my father about Rascal's amusing antics, he said, "I'm afraid you are in for trouble, Sterling." And he was right. Night after night Rascal left my bed and rambled around the neighborhood, raiding nearby gardens. It was not long before an angry delegation came to our house to protest.

They sat in comfortable chairs around my canoe in the living room, sizzling with anger in the August heat.

"I seen that varmint's tracks right in my garden," said Cy Jenkins, the skinflint lumber dealer.

"Like the seven plagues of Egypt," rumbled Gabriel Thurman, the fiery-tempered minister of an odd little congregation.

The threats came whizzing around us like the buzz of angry hornets as Rascal huddled in my lap for protection.

"I'll set a trap, so help me."

"Next moonlight night I'll shoot him."

"Now just a moment," my father said quietly. "I have a suggestion."

Mike Conway was willing to listen. "What do you suggest?"

"If Sterling buys a collar and leash for his raccoon..."

"Not enough," Cy Jenkins growled.

"And builds him a cage . . ." my father added.

Rascal began to whimper, and I looked anxiously from face to face.

Reverend Thurman glowered at my father and thundered, " 'Vengeance is mine, saith the Lord.' "

This struck Mike Conway as amusing. He threw back his head and roared with laughter as the minister grew purple with rage. Soon everyone except Reverend Thurman and Cy Jenkins was laughing.

"Well, it's settled then," my father added. "A collar, a leash, and a cage."

After the neighbors were gone, I said bitterly to my father, "Jails are for criminals, not for good little raccoons."

"You won't need to build the cage just yet," my father said soothingly. "We're going for a two-week trip, 'way up north to Lake Superior. How would you like that?"

"Do you really mean it?" I asked.

"Of course I mean it. You can ask the Conway boys to take care of your war garden and feed Wowser."

I snatched Rascal from the rug and started dancing crazily around the room. We had been given a delay, a wonderful two-week reprieve.

"When can we start, Daddy?"

"Why, tomorrow I suppose," my father said. "I'll just put a sign on the office door."

It took us two days to reach Lake Superior, which is three hundred miles north of our village. I had never seen such a large body of water. Sapphire-blue, and clear and cold, it stretched away like a vast ocean into the distance.

On its clean gravel shore we found more than twenty semi-precious stones known as agates. On the outside, agates were often pitted, and revealed no evidence of their inner beauty. Some of the ones we found my father later sent to a lapidary to have cut and polished, but that was a secret I would not learn until Christmas.

We made our permanent camp several miles back from the lake on a little river known as the Brule. It is one of the most beautiful trout streams in the world, and it winds its way through forests of pine and spruce and hemlock, dashing between granite boulders as old as the world, or moving gently through deep pools where the big trout lie waiting for the fisherman's fly.

We made our camp in a lofty grove of pines, spreading our blankets on the thick layer of fragrant pine needles. We could see the stars twinkling through the overarching boughs, and hear the wind sighing gently through the treetops. Every morning we awoke refreshed and happy to be alive. We took our morning dip in the pool below our camp, and cooked our bacon and eggs on a safe little campfire, built on a bare ledge of granite that extended into the stream.

My father had legal business to attend to in the city of Superior, Wisconsin. So each morning he took his packet of documents and went to court sessions in the big town some twenty miles away. Rascal and I were left to wander and adventure as we pleased. Recent rains had made the forest safe from fire. We had seen no signs of bears, though a few inhabited the woods. My father knew that Rascal and I could swim like otters, if we accidentally fell into a deep pool. And we could scarcely get lost if we stayed along the river or one of its tributaries.

One day we found a patch of delicious blueberries as big as grapes. Rascal helped me pick them, but ate every one he picked. On another day we followed a tributary of the Brule to its source, a little lost lake as round as a dewdrop. There we saw the first doe and fawn we had ever seen in our lives,

wading among the blossoming water lilies. On other days we fished and caught our share of fair-sized trout, but as yet we had caught none of the monster brown trout that I could often see when the sunlight slanted deep into the water.

On the last day of our precious two-week vacation, my father borrowed a canoe from the only cottager who lived along this stretch of the river and we went cascading down the stream, casting our wet flies into the deeper pools. A noisy kingfisher disputed our right to these waters. A mink appeared momentarily on the shore. Rascal stood at the prow of the canoe, enjoying every moment, and sometimes turning to give a "word of advice," as though he were the pilot. I thought how thrilling it would be when I had finished my own canoe. Rascal and I would be afloat every possible moment.

Rounding a bend in the river, we came upon a blueberry patch which looked as though it had been hit by a small cyclone. Then we saw an old rotten tree ripped to shreds, with the honeycomb of wild bees strewn across a gravel bar.

"Bears!" my father said softly.

Around one more bend and there they were! The mother bear was fishing in the rapids below the pool and had just tossed a big trout to her two

cubs, who were snarling and snapping at each other over the fine breakfast. Rascal trembled a little when he saw these big, fierce cousins almost blocking our passage down the stream.

When the mother bear saw us, she growled a deep warning; then, calling to her cubs, she dashed off through the willows and aspens with a great crackling of branches. In a few moments all was quiet again along the little river. Rascal and I had already seen our first doe and fawn; and now we had seen our first bear and cubs.

I thought nothing could top this moment of excitement, but in the very next pool I hooked a huge trout which I had to fight for nearly twenty minutes before bringing it, gleaming and radiant, to my landing net. By the little scale in my tackle box, this handsome trout weighed just over four pounds, almost exactly the weight of my four-month-old raccoon. Rascal's high trill as I landed the fish was like a cheer of triumph.

That night a cold rain whipped through the forest, and we hastily gathered our gear and slept uncomfortably in the car. Next morning we started home through the rain-washed air, a little stiff and damp, but wonderfully refreshed by our two weeks in the magnificent north country.

Autumn

AUTUMN

WHEN WE RETURNED to Brailsford Junction, I realized that there was no way to avoid the sad duty of buying a collar and leash for Rascal, and building him a cage. I had made a promise, and I must keep it.

One of my problems was money. When I counted all my quarters, dimes, and nickels — earned by mowing lawns and selling vegetables — I knew that after buying the collar and leash, and the lumber and chicken wire for the cage, I would be practically bankrupt. It would take me many months to save enough for the canvas to cover my canoe frame, and that meant that the canoe would have to remain in the living room through another winter.

In those days, children had to earn their spending money. No child I knew had an allowance. So it was up to me to finance every purchase. I had even earned the money to pay for my bicycle and my fishing equipment.

At Garth Shadwick's harness shop, I told that kindly man about my problem. He made a beautiful collar and leash for Rascal, and even engraved his name on a silver plate on the collar.

I wasn't certain Rascal would like to have the collar put around his neck. I let him feel it and smell it first, telling him it was his newest treasure. Rascal liked the shining buckle and the feel of the soft leather.

Finally I slipped it around his neck, and to my surprise he didn't struggle or try to nip me. Instead, he sat up on his square little bottom and began feeling the collar the way a woman sometimes fingers her pearls.

I knew that I didn't have enough money to pay Mr. Chadwick adequately, so I put four quarters on his workbench as a down payment and said I would bring him something every week for the next six months.

The harnessmaker looked at Rascal and me over his spectacles and said, "Why, son, I'd be cheating you if I took more than twenty-five cents for that leash and collar. Now get along with your little 'coon. I've got work to do."

Cy Jenkins at the lumberyard was a cat of another color. He had cheated me when I had purchased the lumber for my canoe, but now he pretended to be giving me a bargain in two-by-fours and chicken wire. I trustingly put every cent I had into his hands, and he counted it carefully.

"Comes out right to the penny," he declared, pocketing all my hard-earned money. "But you'd better start building that cage in a hurry. Your 'coon's been stealing my ripe grapes. Seen him with my own eyes."

The lumber and chicken wire were to be delivered the next morning, so Rascal and I still had one glorious afternoon of perfect freedom before I had to begin building his prison. We climbed the oak tree in the back yard on cleats I had nailed like a ladder up the trunk. And there we shared a lunch of jelly sandwiches and listened to the wind rustling through the green leaves around us.

All afternoon I sat in my favorite crotch of the tree reading a book, while Rascal sunned on a nearby limb. We were tree dwellers, hoping that we would never need to touch the ground again. But hunger brought us to earth at last, as the sun sank low in the west.

My father was away on a business trip, so Rascal and I ate supper from the icebox. Then we climbed the tree once more to watch the stars come out. I told my little raccoon everything my mother had taught me about the stars before she died, and I pointed out two constellations, the Great Bear and the Little Bear.

The Great Bear was *my* constellation, so of course the Little Bear was Rascal's by natural right. Then I had a sad but happy thought. After we were both dead, we would go to live in the sky — the Great Bear and the Little Bear swimming across the midnight sky together.

Building a cage for a beloved pet who loves his freedom is like building a jail for a good friend. The work went rather slowly, and I never let Rascal realize what a terrible thing I was doing. He played with pebbles in the postholes I was digging, ran back and forth through the big coils of chicken wire, and thought we were playing a new sort of game.

I planned the cage carefully, twelve feet wide, twelve feet long, and twelve feet high. It enclosed his favorite part of the back yard, including my minnow pool. At one side was his home in the oak tree, and on the other a little door I cut in the side of the barn, just big enough for a raccoon. Inside the barn I enclosed a long-disused box stall, covering the floor with fresh golden straw.

It was necessary to roof both the cage and the

box stall with chicken wire, because a raccoon can climb any fence that was ever built.

For my own entrance into the cage I hung an old screen door between two posts, and also covered this with chicken wire. I used such a stout hook and eye to fasten this door that I was sure my raccoon couldn't unlock it. But even when the cage was finished, I could not bring myself to commit the awful act of putting my pet in prison.

By this time Reverend Gabriel Thurman and other neighbors were likewise complaining that they were losing ripe grapes from their arbors. People scowled at me when I walked along the street with Rascal on my shoulder. Even though he now wore his leash and collar in the daytime, I let him run free at night, and it was during these dark hours that he stole the grapes.

Whenever I was asked crossly when I intended to lock up my raccoon, I would drop my eyes and say, "Maybe tomorrow."

Because so many farm boys were in the American Army, fighting the Germans in France, school opened late in the autumn of 1918. Women and children and old men tried to do the heavy work of harvesting tobacco, corn, and other crops still in the field. From my big war garden I dug potatoes, carrots, and beets, which I sold at the grocery store. This brought me in a little more cash to put in the earthenware crock which I used for a bank, but the silver accumulated very slowly. I knew that I could not earn more than a dollar a week selling *Saturday Evening Posts*. In fact, I would have to wait until the muskrat season opened before I could make the money I needed to buy canvas for my canoe. And I would need a few coins for the Irish Picnic and Horse Fair, the most exciting annual event of the autumn season.

On the land adjoining us to the west lived the Conway family. Mike Conway's stallion Donnybrook was one of the finest trotters in the whole region. Some race horses adopt a cat or a dog as a stable mate. Donnybrook had taken a fancy to Rascal. Whenever my raccoon climbed a post of the paddock, the black stallion immediately became gentle, changing his shrill whinny to a soft whicker. He would trot over to the fence and nuzzle my small raccoon, while Rascal ran his sensitive hands over the big velvet muzzle, fingering the bright rings of the halter.

Rascal and I were as fond of Mike Conway's Donnybrook as we were fearful of Gabriel Thurman's Model-T Ford. The terrible-tempered minister delighted in blowing his loud horn and speeding through horse-drawn traffic. Once he had come dangerously close to us when Rascal and I were riding peacefully down the street on my bicycle.

There was a rumor that Mike Conway, who hated automobiles, had offered to race the minister's Ford around the half-mile oval at the Irish Picnic. Excitement ran high all over town as the crowds gathered at the fairgrounds on a bright September morning.

Rascal and I rode the merry-go-round and the Ferris wheel. Then I entered the blueberry-pie-eating contest. Across the plank table from me was the biggest, meanest, greediest twelve-year-old in town, Slammy Stillman. Many other boys were lined up on either side of the table. Our hands were tied behind our backs, and a big pie was placed before each of us.

Bang! We were off, with a good juicy plunge through the crust and deep into the berries. Pie tins began to slip, and frantic small boys retrieved them with their teeth. The crowd around us was roaring with laughter, but we were desperate, exasperated, and covered with berries. It looked as though Slammy was winning, but just then a friend came to my rescue. Rascal knew all about blueberries, and he loved pie. He jumped up on the table and began eating from the other side of my pie tin, furnishing just enough resistance so that the tin didn't slip. We were gaining on Slammy.

When this big bully looked up and saw what was happening, he leaped to his feet and shouted, "Cheater, cheater, look at that cheater!" Slammy had never played fair in his life, but he was always the first to yell "Cheater!" Rascal and I beat him by several licks. The judges had to disqualify me, however, because of Rascal's help. But I did get a consolation prize, a real league baseball autographed by every member of the local team.

In the afternoon, there was a wild and crazy race between Donnybrook pulling Mike Conway on a sulky and Gabriel Thurman in his Model T — twice around the track for the trotter to three times around the track for the Ford. After the great horse had won, he pulled over to the fence where Rascal and I were waiting, and in front of more than a thousand delighted spectators he nuzzled my raccoon while Rascal trilled his excitement and caressed the big black stallion's muzzle. Twice that day we had tasted victory.

My father was still away in Montana at his wheat ranch. It was the longest time he had ever left me alone, and the house seemed empty and deserted.

I had decided that I could no longer postpone

caging Rascal. I had given him his day of joy at the Irish Picnic, but now I must keep my promise and lock him up. Rascal and I ate supper together in his cage, and I stayed talking to him and petting him for a long time. Then, steeling myself to the dreadful deed, I stepped from the cage and closed and locked the door behind me.

Rascal at first merely asked politely to be let out. Then he suddenly realized that he was trapped, caged, imprisoned. He ran frantically all over the enclosure, crying out to me.

I went into the empty house, but his voice still came to me through the open windows, pleading, terrified — asking for me — telling me he loved me and had always trusted me.

After a while I couldn't stand it any longer, so I went out and unhooked the door and brought him to bed with me. We slept fitfully, touching each other again and again throughout the night, for reassurance.

When the school bell finally rang through the crisp air on a bright morning early in October, I hurried off with my new pencils and books. I always liked the opening of school, and this year it was particularly exciting because I was entering junior high.

I was only sorry to have to lock Rascal securely in his cage during school hours. But Wowser kept him company just outside the fence, and Donnybrook whickered softly from the nearby paddock.

My most interesting teacher that year was Miss Whalen, who loved biology as my mother had loved it. She caught our attention the very first day by asking us about our pets. Almost every boy or girl in class had a dog or cat or pony or canary. But I was the only one with a raccoon. Miss Whalen asked me if I would bring Rascal to school on the following Monday morning.

I combed and brushed him until his fur shone, and I polished his nameplate with silver polish. Rascal sat politely on Miss Whalen's desk, examining a small glass paperweight. I was very proud of his good behavior.

"As you can see," Miss Whalen began, "raccoons are curious."

Then she wrote on the blackboard: "Raccoon — an Indian word meaning 'he who scratches.' "

Slammy Stillman asked if raccoons scratch because they have fleas, and everyone laughed. Miss

Whalen rapped lightly for order, and I raised my hand.

"Yes, Sterling."

"Rascal is perfectly clean. He goes swimming every day," I said, "and he never had a flea in his life."

"I think," said Miss Whalen, "that the Indians meant that raccoons scratch and dig for turtle eggs and other food along the shore."

Then she went on to tell us many things that even I did not know: how raccoons live in every state of the Union, and how they have two to six kits every spring.

"Raccoons are also called 'wash bears,'" she said. "Doesn't Rascal look like a little bear?"

She placed a shallow laboratory pan, containing perhaps an inch of water, on her desk, and in the water she placed a crayfish. Rascal responded immediately. Gazing off through a window, he ran his hands all over the bottom of the enameled pan. Suddenly his body stiffened for a pounce, and two seconds later he had his prey fast in his grip and was washing it happily in preparation for his feast.

Everyone in the class wanted to pet my small raccoon, so as I stood beside him, the boys and girls came by in single file. Some of the girls pretended to be a little afraid. Slammy was the last in line, and he slouched up, shifty-eyed and sneering. Though I was watching for trouble, I was a moment too late. Just as he reached the raccoon, Slammy stretched a heavy rubber band and snapped Rascal in the face.

Very rarely before had I heard Rascal's scream of rage. But now I heard it, a piercing fight-to-the-death cry. A split second later he sank his fine sharp teeth into Slammy's fat hand.

Slammy yelled until you could have heard him in the assembly hall. He danced around, shaking his hand and shouting, "Mad 'coon! Mad 'coon — you gotta shoot him now — mad 'coon!"

Miss Whalen was icy cold. "Here, Slammy, use some of this iodine on your little bite."

Then she turned to me sympathetically. "I'm sorry, Sterling, but you will have to keep your raccoon in his cage day and night for the next two weeks. If he should show signs of rabies, we would still have time to get treatments for Slammy."

"But Rascal isn't rabid," I protested.

"I know, but we can't take any chances."

No longer could Rascal join me after school while I raked leaves or sold my *Saturday Evening Posts*. But I spent every hour that I could in his cage, convinced that if he had to be a prisoner, I would too. Slammy's punctured hand healed almost immediately, and in two weeks Rascal and I could frisk again through the autumn weather and the crimson maple leaves.

Late in October, Spanish influenza, which had swept Europe and the eastern states, hit Brailsford Junction, killing more of our citizens than did the war. Mine was one of the milder cases, but my father was worried. He bundled me into the car and, with Rascal beside me, took me to the North homestead, to the great brick farmhouse where he had spent his boyhood. The farm was now run by my father's brother Fred, his gentle wife Lillie, and their three teen-age boys.

"Why, Sterling, are you sick?" Aunt Lillie asked with concern.

"Just a touch of influenza," my father said, "I thought that perhaps . . ."

"Why, of course. He needs my care. Now come in for a second breakfast. Toast and coffee, and it would take me only a minute to fix ham and eggs."

Aunt Lillie had never been known to refuse a sick child or an orphaned lamb. She was gentle and tender, as my mother had been. She soon had me well enough to ride one of the Shetland ponies, with Rascal sitting in front of me as he had on the wooden steeds of the merry-go-round. As my health returned, Rascal and I explored the whole farm, the great dairy barn and haymow, the grain bins, tobacco sheds where the brown leaves were drying, and, best of all, the honey house where Rascal discovered that honey is almost as delicious as sweet corn.

All too soon the day came when I must go home and return to school. It happened to be my twelfth birthday, and Aunt Lillie roasted a plump young turkey with hickory-nut stuffing. For dessert we had a choice of cold pumpkin pie with whipped cream or hot mince pie fresh from the oven. Rascal and I ate more than our share of every dish on the table.

On November 11, 1918, the Armistice, ending four years of bloody struggle, was signed in France. The "war to end war" had been won. There would never be another conflict. Or so we believed in that far-off and innocent time.

Rascal and I helped celebrate the joyous event. I wove red, white, and blue crepe-paper ribbons through the spokes of my bicycle wheels, put Rascal in the basket, and joined the wild and jubilant crowd. The fire whistle blew continuously, and every church and school bell in town joined the chorus. I rang my bicycle bell to add to the din.

In the afternoon everyone went home, tired but happy, and I began oiling my traps for the muskrat season ahead. Rascal, who was always curious about everything, came over to sniff and feel the traps, and a terrible thought slowed my fingers. I opened one of the illustrated catalogues sent to trappers by the St. Louis fur buyers. There, in full color, on the very first page was a handsome raccoon trying desperately to pull his paw from the jaws of a trap. I, of course, had never trapped a *raccoon.* But how could anyone have the cruelty to mutilate the sensitive hands of an animal like Rascal? I picked up my pet and hugged him to me in remorse.

I burned my fur catalogues in the furnace and hung my traps in the barn, never to use them again. Men had stopped killing other men in France, and on that day I signed my own permanent peace treaty with the animals and birds of the world.

Winter

WINTER

THE FIRST BIG SNOWFLAKES began falling early in December. As cold weather set in, Rascal became drowsy. Raccoons do not actually hibernate, but they do sleep for many days at a time during the winter months.

I lined Rascal's home in the oak tree with an old woolen blanket and an outgrown sweater of mine. Rascal took an immediate fancy to the sweater, perhaps associating it with me. Every morning before I left for school, I paid him a visit. It was comforting to feel his warm, furry body breathing slowly and steadily. Sometimes he awoke and put his black-masked face out of the hole to greet me.

I always rewarded him with a handful of pecans.

As Christmas approached, I began to worry about finances again. How could I possibly pay for the presents I wanted to buy? In previous years I had earned as much as seventy-five dollars trapping muskrats, and this allowed me to buy fine Christmas gifts for every member of the family. But now that I had signed my peace treaty with all living creatures, this source of income had vanished. No matter how many sidewalks I shoveled or *Saturday Evening Posts* I sold, money came in very slowly. And prices were frightfully high in the stores.

One day, after a discouraging round of window shopping, I stopped at the post office and found two letters waiting for me in our box. One was from my soldier-brother Herschel, our first since the shooting had ceased. It was wonderful to find that he was alive and unhurt, and had survived many battles; but he would not be home for many months. He explained that demobilization was a slow process.

The other was from my beloved sister Jessica, still taking graduate work at the University of Chicago. Letters from Jessica were always a joy, so gay and affectionate. She had taken care of my father and myself for a long while after my mother's death, and still was like a second mother to me. She said she would definitely be home for Christmas. And she had generously sent a check for ten dollars to help me with my shopping.

Both letters were cheering, and I began eagerly preparing for the holidays ahead.

My father was away on another business trip. So I cleaned the house and decorated a fragrant spruce tree with gay baubles and icicles and a big silver star. Then, as an afterthought, I fenced off the many-windowed bay where the tree stood. I didn't want my raccoon to break the fragile decorations.

My father was surprised to see the woven wire barrier. But he didn't scold me. However, when Jessica arrived a few days later and was met joyfully at the train, I began to worry. When she entered the living room, I wasn't sure whether she wanted to laugh or cry. Suddenly I saw it all through my sister's concerned eyes. In this comfortable room which she had always kept so spotless — an unfinished canoe laced with bright ribbons, a Christmas tree behind chicken wire, and dust on the furniture.

"Oh, Daddy," she wailed, "you can't go on living like this. You must hire a housekeeper."

"But Jessica," I pleaded, "I worked so hard to clean the house and decorate the tree, and to build

the fence so Rascal couldn't break the ornaments. He's a wonderful raccoon; I know you'll love him."

Then Jessica was laughing and hugging me, and telling me I was an absurd little boy, and I knew that I hadn't spoiled the spirit of Christmas, even with the chicken wire.

On Christmas Eve we lighted the Yule log in the fireplace, so that it shone upon all the glittering decorations on the tree. The wire glistened like a cobweb hung with drops of dew. We brought in Wowser and some selected cats and sleepy Rascal, because we always shared this lovely occasion with some of our pets.

There were catnip mice for the cats — they made old toms and tabbies as playful as kittens. A new collar for Wowser had been made by my friend at the harness shop, and there were Christmas candy and pecans for Rascal. After we had opened all the mufflers, socks, ties, fur-lined gloves, and books, we came to the very special gifts — a fur muff for Jessica, a sheared beaver cap for my father, and — wonder of wonders — shoe-skates for me. I had never before seen a pair of these undreamed-of luxuries.

There were two surprises yet in store. One was in a little leather pouch which my father now brought from his pocket, pouring seven beautifully cut agates into his hand. He had sent these rough stones, which we had discovered at Lake Superior, to a gem cutter in Chicago, and he now selected three for me, three for Jessica, and one for Rascal. We were all delighted.

Rascal's agate, shaped like a marble, glowed brown and amber and red in the firelight. He rolled it between his hands, smelled it, tasted it, then carried it to the corner where he kept all his pennies and other treasures. He came back chirring cheerfully.

The last and best surprise of all was in a big package marked "From Jessica to Sterling, with love." I couldn't imagine what was inside. But when I saw that my sister had given me all the heavy canvas that I needed for covering the framework of my canoe, I was very near to tears. Jessica saved the day.

"Now maybe we can get this canoe out of the living room," she said, roughing up my hair.

Rascal slept with me that night, as a special concession, and I wondered, as we fell asleep, if raccoons can talk at midnight on Christmas Eve as some other animals are said to do.

Spring

SPRING

THE WINTER was long and cold, and there were no real signs of spring until early March, when sap began to run in the sugar-maple trees and the first faint tufts of fur appeared on the pussy willows. High overhead a few flocks of wild geese headed northward toward their arctic nesting grounds.

The whole world was astir after its winter stillness. Soon it would be the season for mating and the rearing of young. The meadow mice broke through the old crust of snow to view the sky. Their big cousins, the muskrats, came from their ponds and streams to nibble on tufts of green along the shore.

Rascal was also aware of the season. He was old enough now to have a mate, and he was becoming increasingly restless. On one moonlight night I heard hair-raising screams of rage. Grabbing a flashlight, I ran out to find Rascal and another undoubtedly male raccoon fighting each other through the chicken wire. On another evening I heard very different sounds, the tender crooning of a female raccoon trying to find her way into Rascal's cage.

During a week of unseasonably warm weather, we put the screens on the windows and doors. On the first night that we left the doors open, Rascal paid me a surprise visit. He had learned how to lift the hook on the entrance to his cage, and of course he had not forgotten how to open the back screen door of the house. He came to my bedroom, chirring happily, and burrowed under the covers. I could have padlocked the cage, but decided against it. Rascal had again earned his freedom, and he deserved it.

However, when on the very next evening my raccoon raided Reverend Thurman's henhouse, I began to realize that my wonderful year with Rascal was coming to an end.

Since Christmas, I had worked hard completing my canoe. I had stretched the canvas tightly over the wooden frame, added trim at prow and stern and around the edges of the boat, and built snug compartments at each end to carry camping equipment, food, or fishing tackle. My friend Art Cunningham, who loved canoeing as much as I did, helped me carry my beautiful slim craft to the flooded creek for its trial run. Enameled a glossy green, it floated like some slim water bird, and at a touch of our paddles darted like a trout into the

current. Rascal again stood at the prow, as he
had during our fast ride down the Brule River. He
still loved speed and danger.

Except for the success of my canoe, I had little
to be happy about during the month of April. Reverend Thurman had his shotgun loaded, waiting
for the next raid on his henhouse. And, as though

this were not enough worry, I learned one day that my sisters Theo and Jessica had finally convinced my father that we must hire a full-time housekeeper.

Mrs. Quinn, who came to inquire about the job, was a hard-faced, middle-aged woman who hated pets and would not allow any animal in the house. She examined our home from cellar to attic and ran her finger over the furniture to show us the dust. Furthermore, she demanded my bedroom for herself.

"That is, if I decide to take the job," she added. "I'll let you know in a couple of weeks."

When I said my prayers that night, I added, "Bless Rascal and Daddy and Theo and Jessica and Herschel. And don't let Reverend Thurman shoot Rascal. And please don't let Mrs. Quinn be our housekeeper."

But I already knew that God usually helps only those who help themselves. In the next two weeks I would have to think of a way to make our life bearable with this grim woman in the house, and I would also have to work out some way to save my greatly loved raccoon.

I moved my things upstairs to a big back bedroom and an adjoining study. I explained to my father that I would make my own bed, clean my own rooms, and let Mrs. Quinn take care of the rest of the house in any way that suited her.

Then I had a small inspiration. The study, opening off the bedroom, was at the very rear of the house. One window at the end of the gable suggested an exciting second entrance to my quarters. Cutting neat cleats, each eighteen inches in length, I nailed them one above another at convenient intervals, making a ladder to the back window. Now my raccoon could visit me at any time of the day or night, and Mrs. Quinn wouldn't even know about it.

When I showed my father this ladder, he merely sighed and suggested that I paint the cleats the same color as the house. I thought this was a brilliant idea, since it made them practically invisible. Mrs. Quinn and my other enemies wouldn't be able to spy them out.

But deep in my heart I knew that none of my plans would ensure Rascal's life. He ran the constant peril of being shot. Besides, he was now a young adult, and was not completely happy as a domesticated pet. I realized sadly that I was being unfair in keeping him from his natural life in the woods.

The two weeks preceding Mrs. Quinn's arrival passed all too swiftly. One pleasant Saturday morning I made my decision. Rascal did not behave very well during breakfast. He walked directly across the tablecloth to the sugar bowl, lifted the lid, and helped himself to two lumps. Thirteen pounds of raccoon on the dining-room table is quite a centerpiece. But knowing what I was planning, I couldn't scold him.

I told my father that Rascal and I would be away all afternoon and evening on a long canoe trip. He looked at us quite sympathetically and said, "Take good care of yourself, Sterling."

Packing a basket of sandwiches, strawberry pop, and soft-shelled pecans, I led Rascal to where my canoe was waiting at the edge of the flooded creek. In a moment we were racing toward the river, with Rascal standing at the prow.

When we reached the river, I turned up the bigger stream, and for hours labored against the heavy current while Rascal slept. He awoke toward sunset as we floated out onto the quiet mirror of Lake Koshkonong. I was headed for a dark, wild point of land where there was everything a raccoon could possibly wish to eat: crayfish, minnows, clams, turtle eggs — a safe wilderness of marsh and forest known as Koshkonong Point, where a large creek of the same name entered the lake.

It was an evening of full moon, much like the one when I had found my friend and brought him home to be my pet. Rascal was a big lusty fellow now, thirteen times the weight of the helpless little creature I had fed warm milk to through a straw. He could climb, swim, and almost talk. And he could catch all the food he needed along any shore. As I thought of all he had learned, I was both proud and sad.

We entered the mouth of Koshkonong Creek and paddled up this stream several hundred feet. The

peepers shrilled, and bullfrogs thrummed their bass fiddles. A little screech owl trilled a note that sounded almost like Rascal's when he had been much younger.

I had decided to let my raccoon make up his own mind. So I took off his collar and put it in the pocket of my corduroy jacket, as something to remember him by if he should choose to leave me. We sat together in the canoe, listening to all the night sounds around us, but for one sound in particular.

It came at last, the same crooning I had heard when the female raccoon had tried to reach him through the chicken wire. Rascal became increasingly excited. Soon he answered with a deeper crooning of his own. The female was now approaching along the edge of the stream, calling to him tenderly. Rascal raced to the prow of the canoe, straining to see through the moonlight and shadow, sniffing the air and asking questions.

"Do as you please, my little raccoon. It's your life," I told him.

He hesitated for a full minute, turned once to look back at me, then took the plunge and swam to the near shore. He had chosen to join the female raccoon somewhere in the shadows. I caught only one glimpse of them together in the moonlight before they disappeared to begin their new life together.

I left the pecans on a stump near the waterline, hoping Rascal would find them. And I paddled swiftly and desperately away from the place where we had parted.